# Dharma the Cat

## Philosophy
## With Fur

Cartoons by David Lourie and Ted Blackall

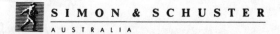
SIMON & SCHUSTER
AUSTRALIA

DHARMA THE CAT
First published in Australia in 2000 by
Simon & Schuster (Australia) Pty Limited
20 Barcoo Street, East Roseville NSW 2069

A Viacom Company
Sydney New York London Toronto Tokyo Singapore

National Library of Australia
Cataloguing-in-Publication data:

    Lourie, David.
    Dharma the cat : philosophy with fur

    ISBN 0 7318 1035 X

    1.Buddhism - Caricatures and cartoons. I. Title

    294.3

Design by David Lourie and Vivien Valk, I Bluedog Design
Cartoons by David Lourie and Ted Blackall

Set in Lifetime
Printed in Australia by Griffin Press

10 9 8 7 6 5 4 3 2 1

With special thanks to Paula Lourie,
Merrilyn Blackall, John Lind, Philip Cohen.

Visit the website
Winner of the 10-Best on the Web award

http://www.DharmaTheCat.com

# Welcome to the
# HOW NOT TO
## School of Wisdom and Insight

**MEDITATE!**

Dharma the Cat observes from a cool place as Bodhi the novice monk stumbles earnestly along his spiritual path, stepping into every possible pitfall along the way — thus kindly shedding a light for us all. Meanwhile, Siam the mouse chases the cheese, and provides spiritual challenges for Bodhi and Dharma.

# CONTENTS

"Time"

6

# DHARMA THE CAT SAYS

Time itself is real, but human perception of time is illusory.
That's one of many human frailties I can
use to my advantage!

"The Lesson"

# DHARMA THE CAT SAYS
Sometimes when you try to teach others,
they end up teaching you.

# SIAM THE MOUSE SAYS
My First Truth is called Diversity: there is more than
one approach to any block of cheese!

9

# DHARMA THE CAT SAYS

One of the human foibles I love most is when people make 'unsolicited announcements' about themselves — when you hear one of these, watch your tail!

# DHARMA THE CAT SAYS
Humans make themselves feel guilty,
but they blame others for it.

"Control"

# DHARMA THE CAT SAYS

Controlling humans is a lot
easier than hunting.

"Non-Attachment"

# DHARMA THE CAT SAYS

It's always so much fun making
Bodhi say 'Aaarghhh!'

"Food for Thought"

# DHARMA THE CAT SAYS
Some thoughts are better left unsaid.

"Non-Conflict"

20

# DHARMA THE CAT SAYS

If you're not willing to do it yourself,
don't ask someone else to.

"Theoretical Practice"

# DHARMA THE CAT SAYS
Theory and practice are worlds apart.

# SIAM THE MOUSE SAYS
Who needs theories OR practice when you've got cheese!

"Spiritual Growth"

24

# DHARMA THE CAT SAYS

Well, master Bodhi believes he has gained the
spiritual mastery necessary to rise above my faux paw —
but, according to him, only this one time!

# DHARMA THE CAT SAYS

He who does my bidding is not
above me in the hierarchy.

## "To Be Or Not To Be?"

# DHARMA THE CAT SAYS
I have the cure — it's fast and sure!

# DHARMA THE CAT SAYS
Comparisons are odious.

# DHARMA THE CAT SAYS
Humans tend to miss the point.

"Catch-22"

# DHARMA THE CAT SAYS

One of the many things separating us cats from humans is our freedom from conceptual thinking.

"The Big Bang?"

# DHARMA THE CAT SAYS

It would be *spiritually* more beneficial for young Bodhi to focus his attention on practical matters, such as how to stay on the path, rather than *seeking* to know things he can't possibly use or verify.

"Tolerance"

# DHARMA THE CAT SAYS
It's easy to be tolerant when
nothing's bugging you.

# DHARMA THE CAT SAYS

Rules, schmools.
Certain types of persons just shouldn't try to
outsmart certain other types of persons!

# DHARMA THE CAT SAYS
Call it what you like — I'm a results man!

# DHARMA THE CAT SAYS
## Pride precedes a fall.

"Opportunity"

# DHARMA THE CAT SAYS

I'm always happy to let someone
rise above their condition.

"Mindfulness"

# DHARMA THE CAT SAYS

When your head's in the clouds,
your feet miss the path.

# DHARMA THE CAT SAYS
## Not all effort is Right Effort!

# SIAM THE MOUSE SAYS

Wise persons don't get any *special treament* around here —
especially when they are on the cheese!

"Manipulating"

# DHARMA THE CAT SAYS
Humans are not without guile.

# DHARMA THE CAT SAYS

So who's lucky?
Remember — a kind nature is its own reward.

"Depression"

# DHARMA THE CAT SAYS

Your suffering won't heal anyone. The cure for *sadness* is giving.
When you're feeling down, find a way to help *someone* else.

# DHARMA THE CAT SAYS

When the Buddha points to where you should look,
don't keep watching his finger.

**Panel 1:** OKAY, DHARMA WANTS TO SEE THE "CATS" VIDEO, SIAM WANTS "THE MOUSE THAT ROARED," AND I WANT "THE LITTLE BUDDHA."

*SO OPEN THE CHEEZITS ALREADY*

**Panel 2:** WE WILL BE DEMOCRATIC ABOUT THIS — WE WILL EACH HAVE AN EQUAL VOTE. HOWEVER, IF THERE IS NO CLEAR MAJORITY . . .

"Democracy"

**Panel 3:** I WILL CAST THE DECIDING VOTE, FOR WHATEVER IS IN OUR BEST INTEREST.

*SO MUCH FOR ANIMAL RIGHTS !*

*BOO ! ROARING MICE FOREVER !*

# DHARMA THE CAT SAYS

Real democracy is elusive.
Democracy as practiced by humans is a power game.

# DHARMA THE CAT SAYS
Bodhi's description of cyberspace applies to everything!

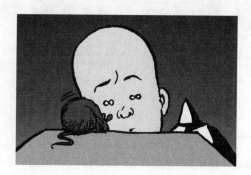

"Labels"

# DHARMA THE CAT SAYS

What you say about others usually applies to yourself.

# DHARMA THE CAT SAYS
### Letting go is hard to do.
### Sometimes you even have to let go of letting go!

# DHARMA THE CAT SAYS

There may be a lot of doorways,
but you won't fit through all of them!

72

# DHARMA THE CAT SAYS
For some, Cheeseville is a lot closer than Nirvana.

# SIAM THE MOUSE SAYS
For some, Cheeseville is Nirvana!

"Voila!"

74

# DHARMA THE CAT SAYS

Sometimes it's helpful to stop collecting new insights,
and to start acting on those you already have.
Insight only has value when acted on.

# WHAT IS BUDDHISM?

The Buddha was born a prince in northern India around 500 BCE. He enjoyed the privileged life of royalty until the age of twenty-nine, at which time he renounced all worldly possessions and dedicated his life to finding a way to alleviate the suffering that was so prevalent in the world outside his royal court. After years of spiritual practice, including fasting and meditation, he realized enlightenment (nirvana), which means he achieved mental clarity and penetrated the illusions of human perception, and became awakened to the true nature of existence. He then travelled throughout India, teaching his ideas and gathering followers who learned his philosophy and practiced his methods of spiritual awakening. After his death his followers formalized his body of teachings, and this became the basis of the religion called Buddhism. Now, some 2500 years later, Buddhist scholars and monks are still debating the exact meaning of many of his teachings. But it is universally agreed that a Buddhist's overall purpose is to live a life dedicated to kindness, compassion, harmlessness and helpfulness, and, by practicing the Buddha's Eightfold Path, to eventually realize enlightenment.

## THE BUDDHA'S FOUR TRUTHS

1. **SUFFERING** and unsatisfactoriness (*duukkha*) are part of life, so pain, loss, grief, frustration, old age and dying are inevitable for everyone.

2. **THE ROOT** of all suffering is craving (attachment to one's desires).

3. **TO END** one's suffering, extinguish the fires of craving and the bonds of attachment.

4. **THE METHOD** to extinguish craving is to practice the Buddha's Eightfold Path – Right View, Right Thought, Right Speech, Right Conduct, Right Livelihood, Right Effort, Right Mindfulness and Right Concentration.

## DHARMA THE CAT'S FOUR TRUTHS

1. **IMPERMANENCE:** In life, the only constant factor is change.

2. **RECIPROCITY:** The qualities you perceive in others are the qualities you draw out in them.

3. **SELF-DESCRIPTION:** People's judgments of others (as opposed to observations) are self-descriptive.

4. **ACCUSATION:** Accusers are guilty.

77

## SIAM THE MOUSE'S FOUR TRUTHS

1. **NON-SINGULARITY:** There is more than one approach to any block of cheese.

2. **NON-CONFLICT:** When those around you fall into conflict, grab the cheese.

3. **UNCERTAINTY PRINCIPLE:** When uncertain about what to do or say, be very still and quiet.

4. **OPEN DOOR POLICY:** When you see an open doorway, go through it.

## BODHI THE MONK'S FOUR TRUTHS

1. **NON-DIRECTING:** Life comes at you from all directions.

2. **NON-CEASING:** Life comes at you at all times.

3. **NON-IMPEDING:** Life comes at you even when you see it coming.

4. **NON-JUDGING:** Life is not impressed or disappointed in you – it's only you that has those feelings.

# BUDDHIST TERMS

**DHARMA** (also *dhamma*): A broad term that has two main meanings – (1) Natural Law, or the way life works; (2) the venerated teachings (either Buddhist or Hindu).

**ENLIGHTENMENT:** This is a relatively modern European term which now refers to the Buddhist idea of realizing nirvana, which is a transcendant state of mental clarity and spiritual fulfillment, or a state beyond suffering. The Buddha's method for realizing enlightenment is his Eightfold Path.

**GURU:** Literally means 'teacher.' In India, the traditional way to embark on a path of spiritual development is to become a disciple of a guru to whom you feel drawn. Becoming a disciple usually requires you to take vows of obedience, chastity, etc.

**KARMA:** Literally means 'action', but in the Buddhist context it must be *intentional* action. Action is either mental (thoughts), verbal (speech) or physical (conduct). The basic idea of karma is expressed well in the North American Native culture as, 'The smile you send out comes back to you'. Your action which is driven by beneficial motives produces beneficial consequences which eventually come back to you. Similarly, your harmful intentions result in harmful consequences which eventually come back to you. The Law of Karma is also referred to as the Doctrine of Cause and Effect, with intention always being the key factor.

**REBIRTH:** When your physical body dies, or becomes empty of life force, your karmic imprint (your lifetime of intentional actions) vitalizes another incipient (as yet unmanifested) life form. This is what triggers that life form's rebirth (its physical manifestation). This Buddhist concept of Rebirth is different from the Hindu concept of Reincarnation, which is based on an eternal soul repeatedly re-manifesting. Buddhism doesn't acknowledge an eternal soul – instead Buddhists favour the relatively impersonal idea of a karmic imprint vitalizing a set of pre-existing conditions.

GET A LIFE !

# DHARMA'S PARTING SHOT
## Don't complain – it's your karma!